Contents

Highlights®
Puzzle BuZz®
Can you find this
buzzing bee?

It is hiding 5 times
on the cover.

COVER ILLUSTRATION BY SCOTT BURROUGHS

Bike Maze

START

Help Kenzie earn her bicycle badge. Find a path from START to FINISH. Do not go past anything blocking your way.

FINISH

Answer on page 30

Can you find these 12 items hidden in this hair salon?

butterfly

sneaker

sombrero

slice of pizza

paperclip

shovel

watering can

saucepan

ladder

spool of thread

duck

golf club

Dot to Dot

Connect the dots from 1 to 36 to make a salon sight.

5

ILLUSTRATION BY DAVE KLUG

Cone Search

Ike has sold a lot of ice-cream cones today! Can you find all 18 cones in this picture?

Do you know?
Are there more chocolate or vanilla ice-cream cones in the picture?

ILLUSTRATION BY DONNA CATANESE

Answer on page 30

Double Bubbles

ILLUSTRATION BY MARK COLLINS

9

Answer on page 31

Wiggle Pictures

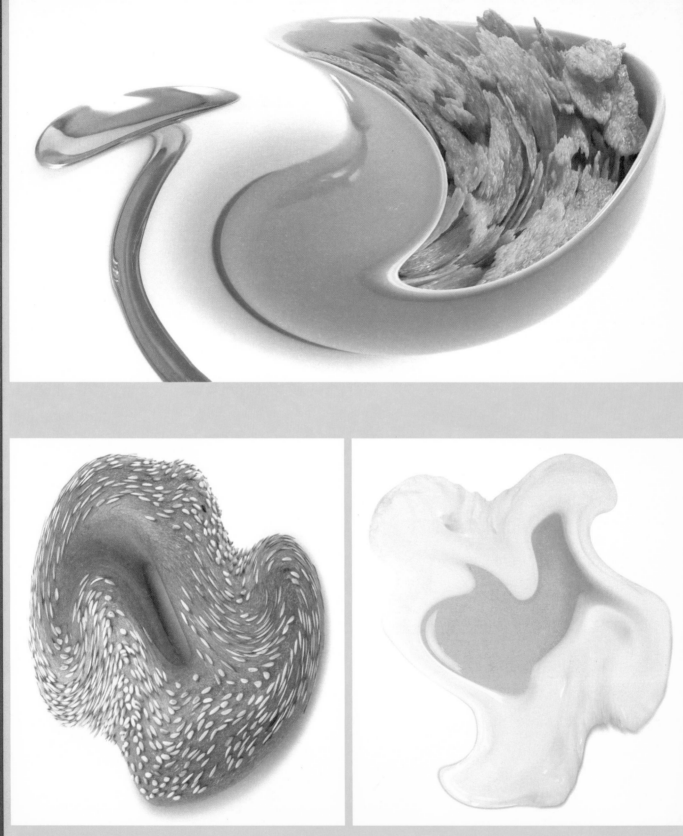

These breakfast foods have been twisted and turned. Can you figure out what each one is?

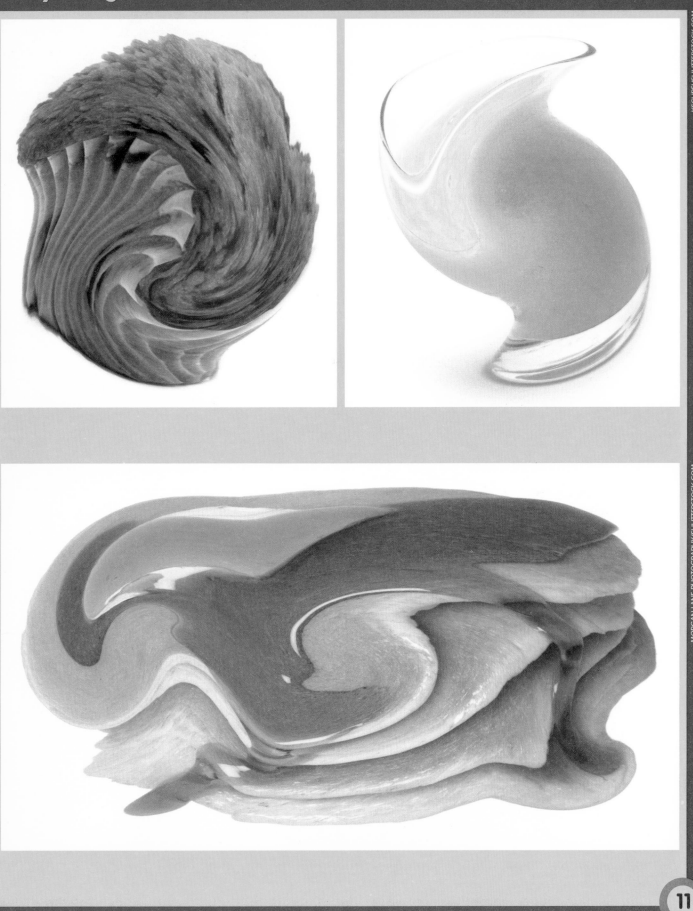

LIZ VAN STEENBURGH/SHUTTERSTOCK.COM

KSCHREI/SHUTTERSTOCK.COM

MORGAN LANE PHOTOGRAPHY/SHUTTERSTOCK.COM

Art Starters

Fill-in Fun Color each space that has a dot to see a fun pair.

Color Copy Use markers or crayons to make a hat that matches.

Use your crayons, pencils, or markers
to finish these art activities.

Step by Step Follow the steps to draw a snail.

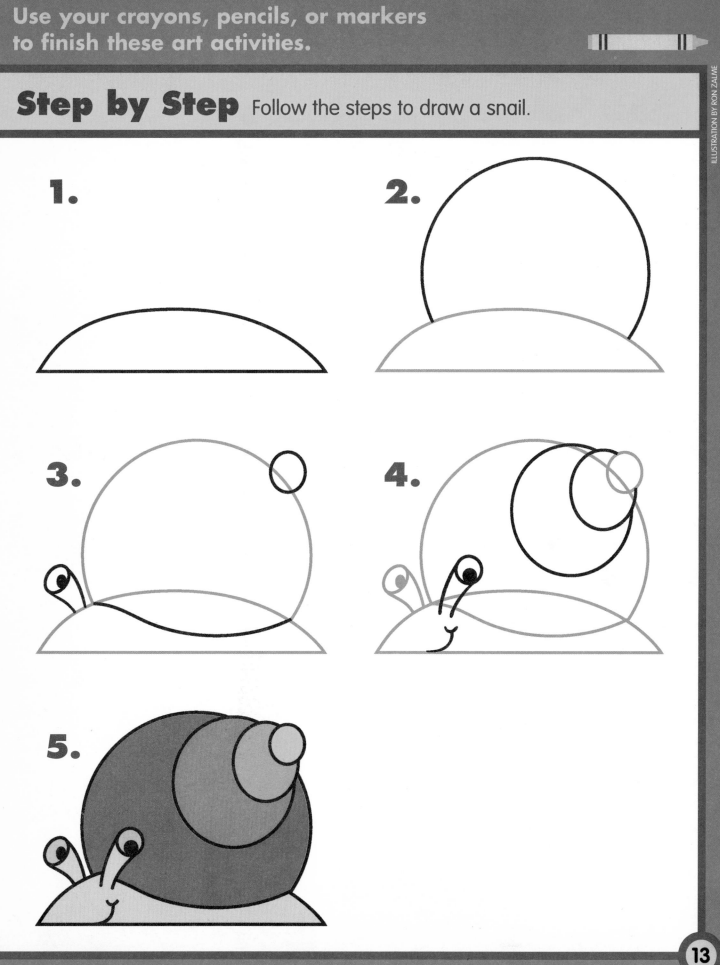

1.

2.

3.

4.

5.

Match Maker

Every dog in the picture has one that looks just like it.
Find all 10 matching pairs.

What's Wrong?®

Highlights **Puzzle Buzz**

Use your stickers to finish the picture. Then see if you can find at least 15 silly things.

ILLUSTRATION BY SEAN PARKES

Answer on page 31

Try 10

1. Name a holiday people celebrate in the summer.

HAPPY

2. How do you say "hello" in Spanish?
- adios
- hijo
- hola

3. Name two words that rhyme with race.

4. Circle the hat with an odd number of points.

5. Name three sounds you might hear at a lake.

6. Circle the item NOT used to make cookies.

7. Which tree's leaves change color in autumn?
○ palm ○ pine ○ maple

8. Name three things you might wear on your feet.

10. In which state will you find Niagara Falls?
○ Nevada
○ New Jersey
○ New York

9. Name four kinds of birds.

ILLUSTRATION BY KELLY KENNEDY

Answer on page 31

Funny Flights

LEMONADE

21

Answer on page 32

Countdown

23

Answer on page 32

ILLUSTRATION BY RITA LASCARO

Time for Dinner

ILLUSTRATION BY R. MICHAEL PALAN

Farm Find

The names of 18 farm things are hidden in the letters. Some words are across. Others are up and down. We found FARMHOUSE. Can you find the rest?

Word List
- BARN
- CORN
- COW
- CROPS
- EGGS
- ~~FARMHOUSE~~
- FIELD
- GOAT
- HARVEST
- HAY
- HORSE
- PIG
- PLOW
- ROOSTER
- SCARECROW
- SEEDS
- SILO
- TRACTOR

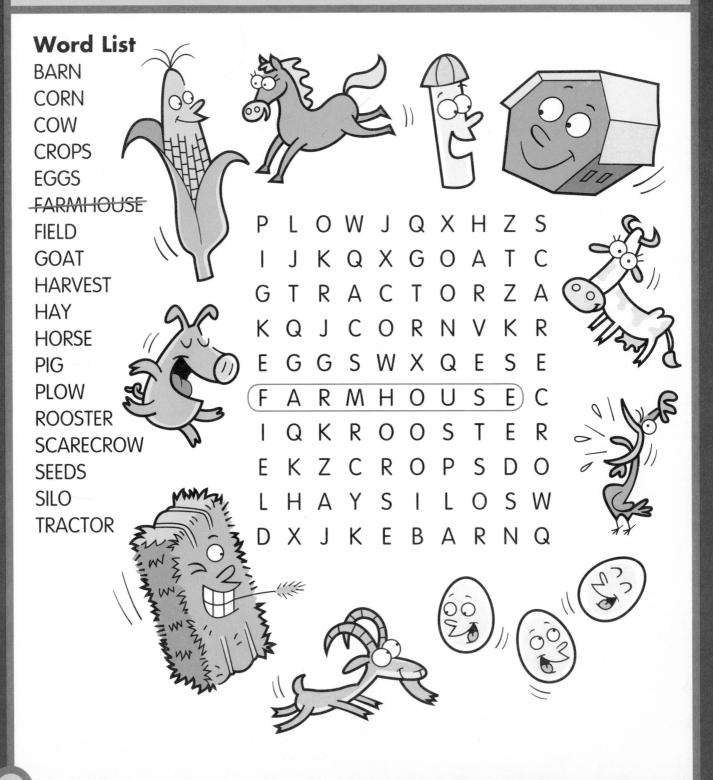

```
P L O W J Q X H Z S
I J K Q X G O A T C
G T R A C T O R Z A
K Q J C O R N V K R
E G G S W X Q E S E
F A R M H O U S E C
I Q K R O O S T E R
E K Z C R O P S D O
L H A Y S I L O S W
D X J K E B A R N Q
```

Highlights Puzzle Buzz

Farm Friends Draw some animals to fill this barnyard.

27

Answer on page 32

Can you find a pig, a pretzel, and a puppy? What other things can you find that begin with the letter P?

ILLUSTRATION BY DAVE KLUG

Tongue Twister

Try to say this three times as fast as you can: **Pirates' private property.**

Answer on page 32

Answers

Cover

2. Bike Maze

Two of a Kind

4. Hidden Pictures®

5. Dot to Dot

6. Cone Search

There are eight vanilla cones and ten chocolate cones, so there are more chocolate ones.

Answers

8. Double Bubbles

10. Wiggle Pictures

bowl of cereal | muffin | orange juice
bagel | fried egg | pancakes

12. Fill-in Fun

It's a baseball and bat!

14. Match Maker

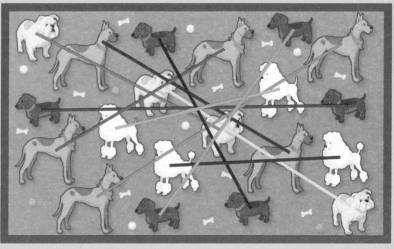

16. What's Wrong?®

Here are the things we found. You may have found others.

18. Try 10

1. Fourth of July
2. Hola
3. Ace and face
   Did you think of others?
4. Circle the hat on the right.
5. Frogs croaking, ducks quacking, waves lapping
6. Circle the drumstick.
7. Maple
8. Socks, sneakers, slippers
9. Cardinal, sparrow, goldfinch, eagle
10. New York

Answers

20. Funny Flights

22. Countdown

24. Time for Dinner

26. Farm Find

P	L	O	W	J	J	Q	X	H	Z	S
I	J	K	Q	X	G	O	A	T	Z	C
G	T	R	A	C	T	O	R	Z	Z	A
K	Q	J	C	O	R	N	V	K	S	R
E	G	G	S	W	X	Q	E	S	E	E
F	A	R	M	H	O	U	S	E	E	C
I	Q	K	R	O	O	S	T	E	R	R
E	K	Z	C	R	O	P	S	D	D	O
L	H	A	Y	S	I	L	O	S	S	W
D	X	J	K	E	B	A	R	N	Q	

28. P Is For ?

Here are the P words we found.
You may have found others.

1. pie
2. pail
3. pear
4. paint
5. pilot
6. plane
7. piano
8. pizza
9. pirate
10. panda

11. parrot
12. pencil
13. paddle
14. pillow
15. pelican
16. present
17. penguin
18. peacock
19. pajamas
20. pennant

21. princess
22. pyramid
23. pumpkin
24. pinwheel
25. pineapple
26. paintbrush
27. pogo stick
28. punchbowl
29. police officer
30. periscope

What Is It?

It's a kitten in a pail!

Highlights Puzzle Buzz